FRIENDSHIP SECRETS

What Don't You

FRIENDSHIP

Know About Your

SECRETS

Best Friend?

Suzanne Weyn

SCHOLASTIC INC.

New York   Toronto   London   Auckland   Sydney
Mexico City   New Delhi   Hong Kong

ISBN 0-439-17622-0

12 11 10 9 8 7 6 5 4 3 2 1   3 4 5/0

Printed in the U.S.A.   40

First Scholastic printing, February 2000

TABLE OF CONTENTS

Introduction......................................1

Basic Bud Questions Switch-off.........................2

Make a BFF Binder..............................9

Discovering a Secret (a hidden talent game)...............11

BFF Hair Makeover Fun...........................17

Bookworms! (a discovery project)......................18

My BFF Would . . . (a matching game)..................19

The Shopping Game..............................26

Rate Your Best Friend (a quiz)....................28

Look to the Stars! Horoscope Fun......................32

Remember This! BFF Memory Quiz......................37

A Few of Our Favorite Things.....................40

2-gether 4-ever? Test Your Friendship Connection.............42

I've Got Your Number: Basic Numerology..................48

Best Friend Truth or Dare.........................52

What to Do? The Help Column Game....................59

Get It Write: Handwriting Analysis...................63

The Psychic Bond: Test for ESP.....................64

I Predict!.................................67

Four Great Ways to Be an Awesome BFF!.............71

FRIENDSHIP

SECRETS

Introduction

She's your **BFF** (**Best Friend Forever**). You sign your postcards, letters, and instant messages **LYLAS** — **Love You Like a Sister**. You mean it, too.

Sure, you two love to **LOL** (**Laugh Out Loud**), but how well do you really know each other?

Did you say, "We know each other totally!"?

Well . . . maybe you do. But you might be surprised what you learn about your best bud when you take the tests and quizzes, and play the games in this book. And that's great! The better you know each other, the closer you'll be.

P.S. You don't *have* to do these friendly activities with your **BFF**. You can do some with other friends, or even with a sister.

Have fun!

1

Basic Bud Questions Switch-Off

Here's how it works. You'll find two copies of the same quiz right here in this book. You get one. Your friend gets the other.

Now fill them out. **But — (this is the important part) — fill out the quiz as if you were your Best Friend.** Where it says name, print her name. Where is says to circle your favorite things, circle the items you think *she'd* circle.

Now switch. How did your friend think you'd fill in this questionnaire? Does she know you as well as she thinks she does?

Talk about what you got right and what you got wrong.

My name is:

(first)_____ (middle)_____ (last)_____.

My mother's name is:

_____.

My father's name is:

_____.

My brother(s) and/or sister(s) are:

(name)_____ (age)_____

_____ _____

_____ _____

I am an oldest /only /middle /youngest child.
(circle one)
I have _____(#) living grandparents.
Their names are:

_____.

Before coming to America, my relatives were from

_____.

3

We have _____ (#) pet(s). Kind of pet(s):

_____

Name of pet(s)

_____

My favorite animal is a

_____.

The most exciting thing I've ever done with my
BFF was

_____

_____

_____.

The best news I've had lately is

_____

_____

_____.

The thing that makes me the maddest is

_____

_____

_____

_____.

2

This is the person who most often makes me angry:

_____.

That's because

_____
_____
_____.

My biggest worry is that

_____
_____
_____.

When I'm grown I'd like a career as a

_____.

I'd like to live here:

_____.

I'd love to visit these faraway places:

_____
_____
_____
_____.

5

My name is:

(first)_____ (middle)_____ (last)_____ .

My mother's name is:

_____ .

My father's name is:

_____ .

My brother(s) and/or sister(s) are:

(name)_____ (age) _____

    _____ _____

    _____ _____

I am an oldest /only /middle /youngest child.
(circle one)

I have _____(#) living grandparents.

Their names are:

_____ .

Before coming to America, my relatives were from

_____.

We have _____ (#) pet(s). Kind of pet(s):

_____

Name of pet(s)

_____

My favorite animal is a

_____.

The most exciting thing I've ever done with my **BFF** was

_____

_____

_____.

The best news I've had lately is

_____

_____

_____.

The thing that makes me the maddest is

_____

_____

_____.

This is the person who most often makes me angry:

_____.

That's because

_____

_____.

My biggest worry is that

_____

_____.

When I'm grown I'd like a career as a

_____.

I'd like to live here:

_____.

I'd love to visit these faraway places:

_____

_____

_____.

Make a BFF Binder

Do you wish you and your **BFF** could be 2-gether 4-ever? Though you'll always be friends, sometimes you have to go your separate ways (different classes, different lunch periods, etc.).

Keep your friend close by turning your binder into a collage of photos showing the two of you having fun together. (You can include a group of friends forever if you want.)

HINT! If you don't have many photos, take some. Use a camera you have or buy a disposable one and take lots of shots. Another way is to locate a photo booth. Those long strips of photo-booth pictures look cool for this project.

Here's What You'll Need:

- a plain binder
- a clear plastic photo sheet, with or without photo pockets
- photos of you and your friend
- glue

Glue the clear plastic photo sheet to the front of the binder. Some of the sheets you find in stores have pockets, some don't. You can use either kind.

For Pocketless — make a collage of you and your friend or friends.

For Photo Pockets — fill the pockets with your photos.

For Both — be creative and add stickers, glitter, words torn from magazines, mementos of your times together, and anything else you can come up with.

> **OIC! (Oh, I see!)** Did you know that August 1 is Friendship Day? Do something nice for your pal.

Discovering a Secret
(a hidden talent game)

What's your friend's secret talent? Play this game and find out.

Here's how. Cut up the cards on pages 14 and 15. Put them in a bag or hat. Take turns picking a card. Each of you has to do what the card says. If the player can't or won't, she receives a score of 0. If she does it, she receives a 10.

If the player wants to improve her score, she can use her turn to shout, "Hidden Talent Alert!" She does not pick a card, but instead, she demonstrates her hidden talent.

At the end of 16 turns, (8 each) you count up your scores. The one with the highest number wins. (It might be a tie. But since you are best buds, you can pretend it's a tie every time.)

HINT! If you get tired of the cards in the book, think of other hidden talents, write them on slips of paper, and use them instead.

Here's What You'll Need:

- the cards in this book
- scissors (to cut them out)
- a banana
- bubble gum

Cards on page 14

13

Carefully cut out these cards.

Point your tongue.

Roll your tongue.

Cross your eyes.

Touch your tongue
to your nose.

Peel a banana
with your toes.

Make a realistic
animal noise.

Touch your nose
with your toes.

Stand on your head.

Touch your elbows together behind your back.	Raise one eyebrow.
Whistle "Twinkle, Twinkle, Little Star."	Snap out the theme song to <u>The Addams Family</u>.
Blow a bubble-gum bubble.	Wiggle your ears.
Recite the names of all seven dwarfs.	Spin a Frisbee or ball on your finger.

16

Be a Super-Best Friend!

We all irk one another from time to time; even the best BFFs get peeved. The solution? Talk about it. Nicely tell your pal why what she did bugged you. Remember, the silent treatment is never a good idea.

BFF Hair Makeover Fun

You love your pal just as she is, but sometimes change is fun.

The two of you can spend an afternoon giving each other new looks when you create new hairstyles. Braid it. Change the part. Try a zigzag part. Use lots of pretty little butterfly clips. Glob on the hair gel. Weave in ribbons. Be creative.

You'll learn a lot about your friend when you see the secret side of her that comes out with a new 'do. Ask questions as you work. Has she always dreamed of looking a certain way? Which celeb has a look she admires? How does she imagine herself looking when she gets older?

Bookworms!
(a discovery project)

♡ **D**ecide on a fun book and read it at the same time as your best bud. Each day, talk about what's happening. (**The Baby-Sitters Club Friends Forever is a great series of books by Ann M. Martin about friendship. So are the Harry Potter books by J.K. Rowling. They feature Harry and his two best friends.**)

Your friend might have a totally different opinion of the book than you do. By discussing it, you'll learn a lot about each other.

📧 Trade favorite books. Lend her the ones you've liked best. Read the ones she's liked best. Talk about them.

🎧 Make a tape of your favorite book by reading it out loud on a tape recorder. This is a great gift if your pal has to take a long train or plane ride. Not only will she get to enjoy the book, but she'll also have your friendly voice keeping her company on the journey.

My BFF Would . . . (a matching game)

Do you know what your best bud would do in every situation? Try this game and find out.

Here's how to play. Photocopy two sets of the following five pages (20–24). You'll see the statements are marked A and B. You fill in the A statements and have your **BFF** fill in the B statements. See how many matches you can make. If you want to keep score, give 5 points for every time one of you gets a *she would* statement correctly matched.

1A. If my BFF had to pick between riding a tiger or swimming with dolphins, she would pick

_____.

1B. If I had to pick between riding a tiger or swimming with dolphins, I would pick

_____.

2A. If my BFF was Cinderella she would

 kick her stepsisters in the shins and refuse to work.

 start her own housecleaning business and get rich.

 make wearing coal dust and cinders the latest fashion.

2B. If I were Cinderella, I'd

kick my stepsisters in the shins and refuse to work.

start my own housecleaning business and get rich.

make wearing coal dust and cinders the latest fashion.

3A. If my BFF were a color, she'd be_____.

3B. If I were a color, I'd be_____.

4A. If my BFF were an animal, she'd be a

_____.

4B. If I were an animal, I'd be a

_____.

5A. If my BFF were faced with a bully, she'd
- talk circles around the bully.
- demonstrate her martial arts skill.
- ignore him or her and just walk away.

5B. If I were threatened by a bully, I'd
- talk circles around the bully.
- demonstrate my martial arts skill.
- ignore him or her and just walk away.

6A. If my BFF were sitting for someone's pet and it died, she'd

🗃️ bury it and say it ran away.

👁️ leave town.

🏠 admit the truth.

6B. If I were sitting for someone's pet and it died, I'd

♡ bury it and say it ran away.

🖼️ leave town.

☎️ admit the truth.

7A. If my BFF walked into a pole in front of a crowd, she'd

🏠 smile and pretend she'd meant to do it for laughs.

🗃️ turn red and run away.

👁️ rub her head and not care that everyone was watching.

7B. If I walked into a pole in front of a crowd, I'd

☎️ smile and pretend I'd meant to do it for laughs.

♡   turn red and run away.

🗃   rub my head and not care that everyone was watching.

8A. If my BFF met her favorite rock star, she

📇   wouldn't care.

🎁   would talk to him/her politely, keeping her cool.

🖨   would scream and then faint.

8B. If I met my favorite rock star, I

☎   wouldn't care.

🗃   would talk to him/her politely, keeping my cool.

♡   would scream and then faint.

9A. If my BFF were a flower, she'd be a
_____.

9B. If I were a flower, I'd be a _____.

10A. If my BFF were an Olympic champ, her sport would be

_____.

10B. If I were an Olympic champ, my sport would be

_____.

OIC! Did you know that a pet can be your best friend? A pet snuggles with you when you're sad and plays with you when you're happy. What more can you ask from a friend?

Be a Super-Best Friend! TV TIME

Watch a TV show together even when you're apart. Call your pal when your favorite show is about to begin. Stay on the line so you can talk about the show while it's on.
Of course, you need adult permission for this. Maybe you can use cell phones or a different phone line so you don't tie up the main family line.

The Shopping Game

You can learn a lot about someone by shopping with her. You get to know her taste, whether she's frugal or extravagant, and if she'll let you have the bargain she spotted first (a true test of friendship). Try this shopping game and see what you can discover about your **BFF**.

Here's What You'll Need:

♡ catalogs or magazines

✄ scissors

💰 fake money from a game or store

To prepare (you can do this alone or with your friend); look through the magazines and catalogs you've selected. Find pictures of products you'd like to have. Clothing. Cars. Electronics. Toys. Books. Videos. Anything that appeals to you.

Cut out the pictures.

Now, you and your pal sit facing each other. Each of you holds an equal amount of the play money.

One by one you put a cutout picture between you. One of you says, "I want that and I'll pay (whatever amount) for it."

If you don't also want the item you say, "Fine."

If you do want the item, you challenge, saying, "I want that, too. And I'm willing to pay (a higher amount than your friend was about to pay)." Your friend can then say, "Fine." Or she can offer an even higher amount.

You go back and forth in this way until one of you finally buys the item. The person who buys it takes the pictured item and puts her money in a separate pile or bank.

When one person runs out of money, the other player has the chance to buy up the rest of the pictures at "sale" prices — which means she can pay as little as she likes for them.

For the final scoring, each item is worth 1 point. The person with the most points wins, but winning isn't the point. Getting to know each other better is.

Rate Your Best Friend (a quiz)

How does your best bud rate as a pal? Take this quiz and find out.

1. I can tell my friend

  a. everything.

  b. some things, but not anything super-personal.

  c. only things I want the whole school to know.

2. My pal

  a. always backs me up if I fight with someone.

  b. doesn't take sides if I'm fighting with someone else.

  c. usually defends the person I'm fighting with.

3. I'd lend my BFF

  a. anything she wanted.

  b. some things, but not my best things.

  c. nothing, she destroys everything.

4. My best bud tells me

  a. everything.

  b. most of her secrets.

  c. nothing, her life is a total mystery to me.

5. If we both had a crush on the same boy, my friend would

   a. find a new crush.

   b. want to talk about it and see who liked him most.

   c. flirt outrageously, saying she saw him first.

6. If my pal thought I'd done something wrong, she'd

   a. speak to me about it in private.

   b. act like she didn't care.

   c. accuse me in front of everyone.

7. If my friend broke something of mine, she'd

   a. replace it.

   b. say she was sorry but not replace it.

   c. lie about it.

8. When I leave a message for my friend to call me back, she

   a. calls the moment she gets the message.

   b. calls when she gets around to it.

   c. often doesn't call back.

9. When someone compliments me, my friend

   a. agrees.

b. says why she deserves a similar compliment.

c. disagrees.

10. When my pal and I make a mess in my room, she

a. always helps to clean it up before she leaves.

b. sometimes helps to clean.

c. says my room was already a mess so she doesn't have to help.

11. If someone insults me, my BFF

a. leaps to my defense.

b. calls that person names once he or she has left.

c. says that the person may have a point.

12. I can count on my friend

a. 100% of the time.

b. if she's in a good mood.

c. to let me down.

Your Results

Mostly A's. If you picked A six or more times, you have a terrific best friend. Take good care of this friendship by being the best best friend you can. This **BFF** is worth the effort

Mostly B's. If you have six or more B's, you and

your friend are close, but sometime you'll need to sit down and have a serious discussion. Talk about ways you can make your friendship stronger. Keep up your other friendships (always a good idea, no matter what) because your BFF isn't completely reliable.

Mostly C's. Did you score six or more C's? If so, your **BFF** isn't all a best friend should be. You can stay friendly with her, but don't consider her your bosom buddy. Keep looking for your real soul sister to come along. (Don't worry, she will.)

Be a Super-Best Friend!

On your best bud's birthday, decorate her locker with balloons, cards, and crepe paper. (Check with a teacher a day or two beforehand.) Make a big sign that reads HAPPY BIRTHDAY.

Be there to sing "Happy Birthday!"

HINT! If your BFF has a summer birthday, celebrate her half birthday and really surprise her.

Look to the Stars!
Horoscope Fun

What's your astrological sign? It depends on the day and month you were born. Different signs are said to possess personality traits particular to that sign.

People of a certain sign are also said to make special friends with people of certain other signs. (For example, people born in Cancer get along easily with people born under the sign of Scorpio.)

If — according to astrology — you are supposed to get along well with your **BFF**, you can say, "See? This proves we're meant to be friends!"

If it says you don't get along, say, "How dumb! Who believes this crazy stuff, anyway?"

Either way, it's just for fun. Look below to see what the stars say about you, your friend, and your friendship.

OIC! If your birthday falls between the 22nd and 27th of the month, you're said to be on the cusp. It means you possess traits from both signs on either side of your birthday.

Aquarius, the water bearer (Jan. 20 - Feb. 18):

Idealistic. Open-minded. Unselfish. Fast learners. Sometimes unrealistic. They are faithful and devoted friends. They make good friends with Gemini, Libra, and other Aquarians. They may *think* they like Leos, but that friendship doesn't always work out.

Pisces, the fish (Feb. 19 - March 20):

Imaginative. Creative. Bright, even brilliant. Sometimes confused. Your Pisces friend may baffle you when she says one thing, then does the opposite. Makes good friends with Scorpio and Cancer.

Aries, the ram (March 21 - April 19):

Active. Daring. Responsible. Motivated. Unafraid. Loves flattery. Is sometimes conceited. Loyal. Does well as a friend to Leo and Sagittarius.

Taurus, the bull (April 20 - May 20): Loves beauty. Creative. Enjoys working with hands. Forceful. Decisive. Sometimes close-minded. Your Taurian friend likes to be around lots of people, so be prepared to share her. Taurus does well with Capricorn and Virgo. Taurians like other Taurians, but sometimes they lock horns in bitter disagreement and neither one will give in.

Gemini, the twins (May 21 - June 21): Talented. Restless. Athletic. Unpredictable. Sometimes moody and indecisive. Your Gemini friend likes a person who is dynamic and interesting. Geminis do well with Aquarius and Libra. She may develop a brief interest in Sagittarius and other Geminis, but these friendships often burn out quickly.

Cancer, the crab (June 22 - July 22): Intelligent. Hesitant. Considerate. Sometimes self-doubting. Prefers to spend one-on-one time rather than socializing in groups. Cancers do well with Pisces and Scorpio.

Leo, the lion (July 23 - Aug. 22): Affectionate. Caring. Loyal. Energetic. Generous. Sometimes bad-tempered. Your energetic Leo pal will lead you into lots of fun activities. Leos tend to like Aries and Sagittarius. Friendships with Aquarians don't often last because Aquarius doesn't like the quick Leo temper.

Virgo, the Virgin (Aug. 23 - Sept. 22): Intelligent. Creative. Adaptable. Sensible. Independent. Sometimes seems coldhearted. Your Virgo friend sees you as you really are and likes you just the same. Virgos make good friends with Taurus and Capricorn. They don't gel well with Pisces or other Virgos.

Libra, the scales (Sept. 23 - Oct. 23): Fair-minded. Honest. Creative. Caring. Sometimes lazy. Your Libran **BFF** will always consider your feelings, and she will expect the same from you. Librans do well with Aquarius, Gemini, and other Librans.

Scorpio, the scorpion (Oct. 24 - Nov. 21):

Energetic. Intense. Idealistic. Sometimes vain. Your Scorpio pal might make you mad, but she's the most loyal friend on earth. Scorpios get along well with Cancer, Pisces, and other Scorpios.

Sagittarius, the archer (Nov. 22 - Dec. 21):

Friendly. Sincere. Outspoken. Unselfish. Sometimes insulting. Your Sagittarius friend will always tell you honestly what she thinks. Sagittarius makes good friends with Aries and Leo. Tends to like Geminis but doesn't communicate well with them.

Capricorn, the goat (Dec. 22 - Jan. 19):

Practical. Ambitious. Good memory. Sometimes unforgiving. Your Capricorn pal likes to plan things, like well-run parties. Capricorns get along easily with Taurus and Virgo. Capricorns often *think* they like Cancers, but they clash before too long.

Remember This!
BFF Memory Quiz

How well do you remember what's in your friend's room? Try this memory quiz and see. Go into your friend's room. Then, when you come home, try to answer the questions on the next two pages. After you're done, go back to check and see how well you did. What does your friend's room tell you about her personality?

What's on the walls?

_____

_____

_____

What things are on her dresser?

_____

_____

What color is her bedspread? If it's a pattern,
what does it look like?

_____

_____

_____

What's her bed like? (circle one)

       full   bunk

       single   trundle

       queen   canopy

other (describe)_____

_____

What's on her floor?

_____

_____

Besides a bed and dresser, what other
furniture, if any, is in her room?

_____

_____

Is there a lamp? What does it look like?

_____

I Will Remember You!

Can you remember your friend's face when she's
not around? Use the outline on the next page to
find out. Fill it in with crayons, markers, or colored
pencils and then check to see how accurate you
were. Fill in the blanks first as a reference.

Hair color:_____

Hair style:_____

Eye color:_____

Freckles: yes   no   (circle one)

Braces: yes   no   (circle one)

Earrings: yes   no   (circle one)

Beauty marks: yes   no   (circle one)

A Few of Our Favorite Things

Some friends are so alike they're practically clones. Other friends couldn't be more different. Which type are you and your friend? Fill in the list on the next page. Then fold your answers back and have your friend fill in her favorites. Compare and see the ways you're alike and the ways in which you're different.

FAVORITE	MY FRIEND'S ANSWERS	MY ANSWERS
Color	_____	_____
Flower	_____	_____
Bird	_____	_____
Song	_____	_____
TV Show	_____	_____
TV Star	_____	_____
Movie	_____	_____
Movie Star	_____	_____
Musical Group	_____	_____
Solo Singer	_____	_____
School Subject	_____	_____
Drink	_____	_____
Place	_____	_____
Animal	_____	_____
Holiday	_____	_____
Season	_____	_____
Book	_____	_____
Sport	_____	_____
Food	_____	_____

2-gether 4-ever? Test Your Friendship Connection

We like to say "forever" when we talk about our friends. But some friendships are more long-lasting than others.

Take this test and see how likely you are to still be best friends when you're old and gray.

1. You've had a crummy day. Your teacher yelled at you, your new haircut stinks, and your little sister scratched your new CD. You

    a. call your **BFF**. She's the only person who can make you feel better.

    b. talk to your mother. She's helpful at times like this.

    c. scratch one of your little sister's CDs.

2. You and your BFF wear the same outfit to a party without even discussing it. You

    a. love the fact that you are both wearing the same thing.

    b. aren't surprised, after all you did buy them together.

    c. are surprised that you both made the same choice.

3. Another girl at school invites you to a party without your BFF. You

    a. accept and ask if it's okay for your pal to come, too.

23

b. tell your friend you were invited so she'll
know how popular you are.

c. go to the party but don't tell your
friend.

4. When the two of you talk about serious world
topics, you

a. never agree with your pal. You can't always
understand why she feels the way she does
about things.

b. understand your friend's point of view
but don't always agree.

c. almost always see things the same way.

5. It's Saturday afternoon. What's your idea of a
perfect plan?

a. Doing something with your friend, just
the two of you.

b. Joining a group of kids.

c. Hanging out with a group, then going to
your house with your **BFF**.

6. A neighbor asks if you and your friend would help out in a clothes drive for needy kids. You want to, but would you accept for your friend?

    a. Yes. You know your friend would want to help.

    b. Not sure.

    c. No. It's not the kind of thing she likes.

7. It's your friend's birthday. You

    a. know exactly what to get her.

    b. have no idea what she'd like.

    c. have already found — weeks ago — the perfect thing.

8. The last time you and your pal watched a funny flick together, you

    a. both cracked up at all the same parts.

    b. laughed at totally different things.

    c. laughed because her laugh made you laugh.

9. You and your best bud are studying together for a test. She's getting most of the answers wrong. Do you tell her she's in trouble?

   a. Definitely. You're totally honest with each other.
   b. Maybe. You don't want to hurt her feelings.
   c. No way. She'd be mad at me.

10. Whenever you and your friend talk about your feelings, you come away thinking,

   a. Hmmm, I never knew she felt that way.
   b. We're so much alike!
   c. We never seriously talk about feelings.

11. If you were to describe your BFF to someone, you'd say

   a. "She's really popular!"
   b. "She's fun to hang out with."
   c. "She's just like me."

12. If your relationship was food, yours would be

   a. pizza and pepperoni—made to go together.

   b. candy—sweet but you can't take too much of it.

   c. oil and vinegar—even though we sometimes separate, we go well together.

Scoring

1. a=3 b=2 c=1	7. a=2 b=1 c=3
2. a=3 b=2 c=1	8. a=3 b=1 c=2
3. a=3 b=2 c=1	9. a=3 b=2 c=1
4. a=1 b=2 c=3	10. a=2 b=3 c=1
5. a=3 b=1 c=3	11. a=1 b=2 c=3
6. a=3 b=2 c=1	12. a=3 b=1 c=2

Now add up your score and see how you did.

Friends Forever! 27-36 points. You guys go so well together it's almost scary. Chances are your friendship will last a lifetime. Even if you move far away you'll stay in touch by mail, phone, and instant message. When you're older, you'll plan vacations together so you can see each other.

Best Buds! 20-26 points. You're not the same, but you complement each other. Where she's weak, you're strong, and vice versa. If you move to a different town, or even a different school, that could bust you up. You'd have to make that extra effort to stay together. In fact, you always need to put out that extra energy to talk about things and stay in sync with each other, but it's worth the effort.

Fast Friends! 12-19 points. This friendship is a lot of fun right now, so enjoy it. It may not last out the year, though, unless the two of you can go deeper in honesty, trust, and respect. Don't be discouraged if this friendship doesn't last — finding your **BFF** often takes time and patience.

I've Got Your Number: Basic Numerology

Numerology is similar to astrology. Some people believe it works. Others think it's silly. The idea is that everyone has a number based on birth date. Here's how to find your pal's number.

1. Write down her birth date in number form. Say it's 10/8/1988. Add 10+8+1988. You'll get 2006.

2. Add those numbers: 2+0+0+6. You'll get 8. This means your friend is a #8-type person. It might take you more steps than this to get to a single number — it depends on the birth date — but just keep splitting up your numbers and adding them until you come to a single digit.

3. Now look up your friend's birth number in the section below.

BIRTH NUMBERS

1. **Ones are real individuals.** They can be very single-minded when it comes to achieving goals. They are also trustworthy, ingenious, and capable of great concentration. They can seem conceited and narrow-minded, but they make loyal friends.

2. **Twos believe in justice and equality.** Your #2 friend will be sympathetic to your problems. Don't take advantage of her sweet, fair nature. She might sometimes anger you with her laziness.

3. **Threes are considered survivors.** They stand up well under pressure. They are reliable in a crisis. Your #3 pal will like to have lots of people around her. If you are the possessive type, this could be a problem.

4. **Fours are balanced and poised.** They are honest and not easily tempted to break rules. Sometimes fours are considered boring. You will have to take the lead if you want to go on a sudden, unexpected adventure.

5. **Fives are full of life.** They tend to be adventurous and athletic. On the downside, they don't always look before they leap, resulting in broken bones and broken hearts. Be prepared to sign casts and be a shoulder to cry on.

6. **Sixes are creative idealists.** They have a cheery nature but seek perfection. Sometimes they don't

see dangers that are in front of them. Your #6 friend might be tempted to dump the friendship if she doesn't think it's perfect. Remind her that nothing is.

7. **Sevens are mysterious.** They like to study mystic sciences such as astrology and numerology. Be prepared for your #7 friend to say, "Come in," before you knock because this number is thought to have psychic ability.

8. **Eights are practical people.** They are scientific, sensible, and skeptical. Your #8 friend might offend you with her bluntness, but think about her opinion anyway. Guaranteed, it's logical and well thought out.

9. **Nines are well rounded and many-faceted.** But they are restless and not satisfied with one thing for long. Your #9 friend may not be a friend forever, since she will be tempted to move along to a series of new pals.

Best Friend Truth or Dare

Want your pal to reveal some of her secrets? Try a game of Truth or Dare. You and your **BFF** can play this together or with a group of best pals.

Here's how to play with just one other person. If you're playing with more than one, just keep moving to the next person.

To prepare — Photocopy the Truth! and Dare! pages that follow. Put them on the floor facedown, side by side.

These pages are just to get you started. When you want new Truths and Dares, make them up yourself.

To play —

1. You and your pal sit across from each other.

2. You ask your friend, "Truth or dare?"

3. She answers either "Truth!" or "Dare!"

4. If she selects Truth! she must pick up the Truth! page and answer the first question honestly. If she picks Dare! she must do the first thing on the Dare! page.

5. When she's done, she asks you "Truth or dare?" and it's now your turn to decide.

6. Keep going down the list on both the Truth! and Dare! pages.

54

Truth!

55

Truth!

- Have you ever told a secret someone asked you not to tell? What was it?
- Who do you have a crush on right now?
- What's the wildest thing you want to do someday?
- Have you ever lied to your parents? What did you say?
- What's the dumbest question you ever asked?
- Who would you trade places with if you could?
- When were you the most scared?
- What was your most embarrassing moment?
- Did you ever fake being sick to stay home from school?
- What grosses you out?

Dare!

57

Dare!

- Cross your eyes and touch your tongue to your nose.
- Do a really dumb laugh for one minute.
- Sing the theme song from a TV show.
- Read something while pretending to have a foreign accent.
- Walk across the room with a book balanced on your head.
- Imitate a teacher.
- Pretend a colony of ants just crawled down your pants.
- Make up a rap song about yourself and sing it.
- Make your ugliest or silliest face.
- Pretend your pillow is the love of your life and kiss it.

What to Do?
The Help Column Game

On an afternoon with nothing to do, try this with your **BFF**. Pretend you're writing a Help Column for the local paper. What would you advise a person with these problems to do?

You read the first problem to your friend. She gives her opinion. Then you give your opinion. You can then discuss the problem. When you think you've solved it, move on to the next one. Let her read it, just to keep things lively.

By the end of this session, you'll know a lot about how your **BFF** thinks and feels. You might even discover a few things you didn't know about yourself.

Problem 1

My best friend told everyone at school that I'm adopted. Now the kids are all asking me questions about being adopted. It makes me feel funny. What should I do?

Problem 2
My best friend has started smoking. She wants me to smoke, too. I don't want to and I don't want to tell on her, either, but I hate what she's doing to herself. What should I do?

Problem 3
I have a new best friend. I still like my old best friend and I don't want to hurt her feelings. But I don't want to hang out with just her. My new best friend doesn't like her. What should I do?

Problem 4
I can't keep a secret. People tell me things in private but I can't keep my mouth shut about it. I tell myself that the person I'm telling won't say anything to anyone, but it never works out that way. What should I do?

Problem 5

My best friend is a boy. It's not romantic. We've been friends since we were little. Now the kids have started teasing us and saying we're boyfriend and girlfriend. What should I do?

Problem 6

My friends all tell me I'm too bossy. I don't mean to be, I'm just full of ideas that I think will work. What should I do?

Problem 7

My **BFF** and I like the same boy. He's friendly to both of us. I don't want to lose her friendship, but I like him so much. What should I do?

Problem 8

I have the feeling that my parents like my little brother more than me. It bugs me so much that I'm sometimes mean to him. He's not really a bad kid and I don't want to hurt him, but I can't help myself. What should I do?

Problem 9

My best pal has suddenly discovered boys. It's all she talks about and even thinks about. To be honest, I'm not all that interested. In fact, I'm getting pretty bored. What should I do?

Problem 10

A girl in my class is always criticizing my clothing. She does it in front of everyone, too. This girl acts like she's Miss Fashion, but I don't think she looks so hot. I like the way I look. What should I do?

Problem 11 (Write a real problem here that one of you has.)

_____

_____

_____

_____

_____

_____

_____

Problem 12 (Space for another real problem)

_____

_____

_____

_____

_____

_____

_____

_____

Get It Write: Handwriting Analysis

Did you know that your handwriting reveals secrets about your personality? The study of handwriting is called graphology. Detectives use it to find out things about criminals. Employers use it to tell them things about people they're considering hiring. And you can use graphology to learn personality secrets about your best friend.

Go to the library or bookstore and look for a book on graphology, also called handwriting analysis. Find one that tells you how to interpret different hand-writing styles.

You'll learn that the way we shape letters tells a lot about who we are. Spacing and position on the page also reveal personality secrets. A person who writes way off the line is imaginative and likely to daydream. Someone who dots her i's right over the letter is sensible, while a person who dots them far away from the actual letter is creative.

Have your friend write a few simple sentences, then use your book to uncode the secrets of her personality. To be fair, you should let her analyze your handwriting as well. You might be amazed by how much your writing will tell her about you.

The Psychic Bond: Test for ESP

Do you and your friend have it? You might. Has your friend ever called you just as you were about to punch in her number? Have you ever both said the same thing to each other at the same moment?

People who are close to each other often have a special connection. They feel the other person's emotions or thoughts. This is sometimes called mind-reading or ESP (extrasensory perception).

It helps if one or both of you have a touch of ESP. Some people say there's no such thing as ESP — that it's all coincidence. Other folks are sure it exists. Some of the believers are even scientists who test for it.

Here's a way you and your friend can test yourselves for psychic ability. Be warned — if you both have it, it will be very hard to keep any secrets from each other. But maybe that's a good thing.

The Test
Here's What You'll Need:

- a deck of ordinary playing cards
- your friend
- two rooms next to each other
- two sheets of paper
- two pens or pencils

Choose five cards from each of the deck's four suits. This will give you 20 cards in all. Give the cards to your friend. Instruct her to go into the next room, where she will shuffle and cut the cards, then lay them facedown in a pile.

Once you are both in separate rooms, your friend should pick up the top card and shout "Ready!" loud enough for you to hear. She should write down the card she's holding, then concentrate hard on the picture on the card.

At the same time, you should try to receive a mental image of the card your friend holds. Close your eyes. See what picture pops into your head. When you have an image, write down what card you think it is. Even if you only have part of an image, write it down.

When you've written down your answer, call out, "Next!" The two of you will then try again on a different card. Keep this up until all 20 cards have been drawn. Then compare your list of cards with your friend's list.

Scientists say that one correct guess out of five

can be due to chance. But, if you score two or more out of every five, something more than chance is at work. If half or almost half of your answers match — that something could be ESP.

I Predict!

What does the future hold for you and your **BFF**? Fill in the predictions on the next three pages. You can do this alone or together. Then tear the pages out and stick them in a book or a drawer. Look at them in the future and see how wrong — or right — you were.

Near-Future Predictions

I think this year will be great/good/awful (**circle one**) for us because

_____

_____

_____

_____.

I predict that we will do this fun thing together:

_____

_____.

I think we will have to solve this problem:

_____

_____

_____

_____.

The person who will annoy us most this year will be:_____

_____.

The hardest thing we'll have to do this year will be:

_____.

I predict my pal will do these three things this year:

1._____

_____.

2._____

_____.

3._____

_____.

I predict I will do these three things this year:

1._____

_____.

2._____

_____.

3._____

_____.

Far-Future Predictions

I think my friend and I will/won't (**circle one**) stay friends as adults. I think her career will be:

_____.

My career will be:

_____.

She'll want to live in the city/suburbs/country/a foreign country/the jungle/on another planet (circle one or more).

I'll want to live in the city/suburbs/country/a foreign country/ the jungle/on another planet (circle one or more).

If she has kids, she'll name them:

_____

_____

_____

_____.

If I have kids, I'll name them:

_____

_____

_____

_____.

One way we'll keep in touch is by meeting every year in this special place:

_____

_____

_____

_____.

Four Great Ways to Be an Awesome BFF!

Want to know the best gift you can give your **BFF**? It's to be someone she can feel proud to call her friend. How do you do that? By being the best *you* possible.

Here are some ideas on how:

1. Know yourself. Become familiar with what things you really love. Develop your own hobbies. Enjoy spending time alone.

2. Be active. Do the things you like. These don't have to be the same activities your friend enjoys (although they can be).

3. Be interested in lots of people. Sure, you and your **BFF** have a special bond. But she's not the only person on earth. Get to know others as well. This makes you a more well-rounded person, and you won't be stranded and lonely when your best bud can't be with you.

4. Love yourself. No, that doesn't mean be

conceited. It means respect the unique, lovable person that you are. Take care of your grooming. Don't let others take advantage of you. Stick up for yourself. If you're okay with you, other people will be, too.